HEINEMANN MATHEMATICS 2

Name

SHAPE WORKBOOK

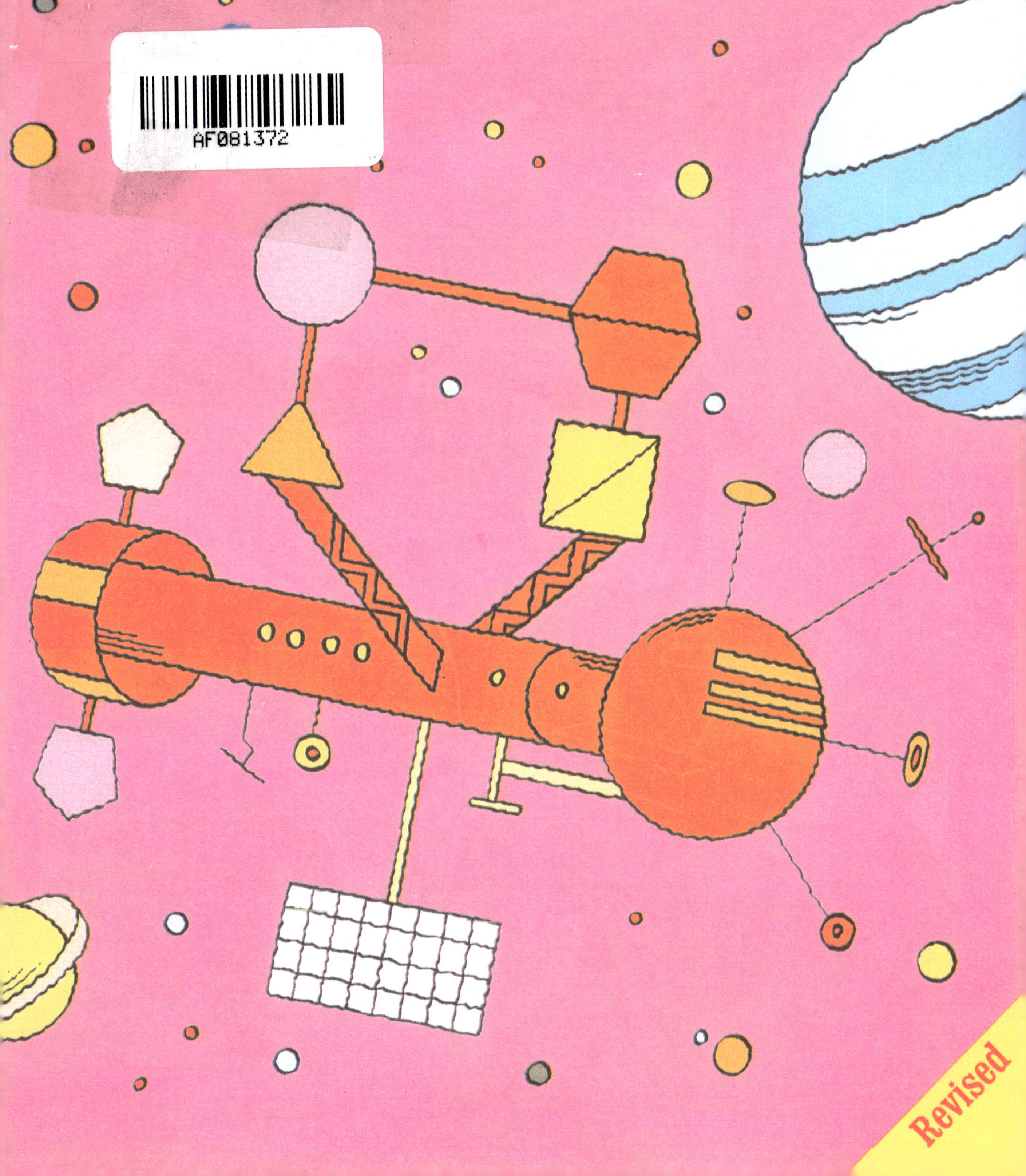

Revised

Mixed bags

Colour to sort.

How many?

__5__ cubes

___ pyramids

___ spheres

___ cuboids

___ cylinders

___ cones

Box of sweets

Match and colour.

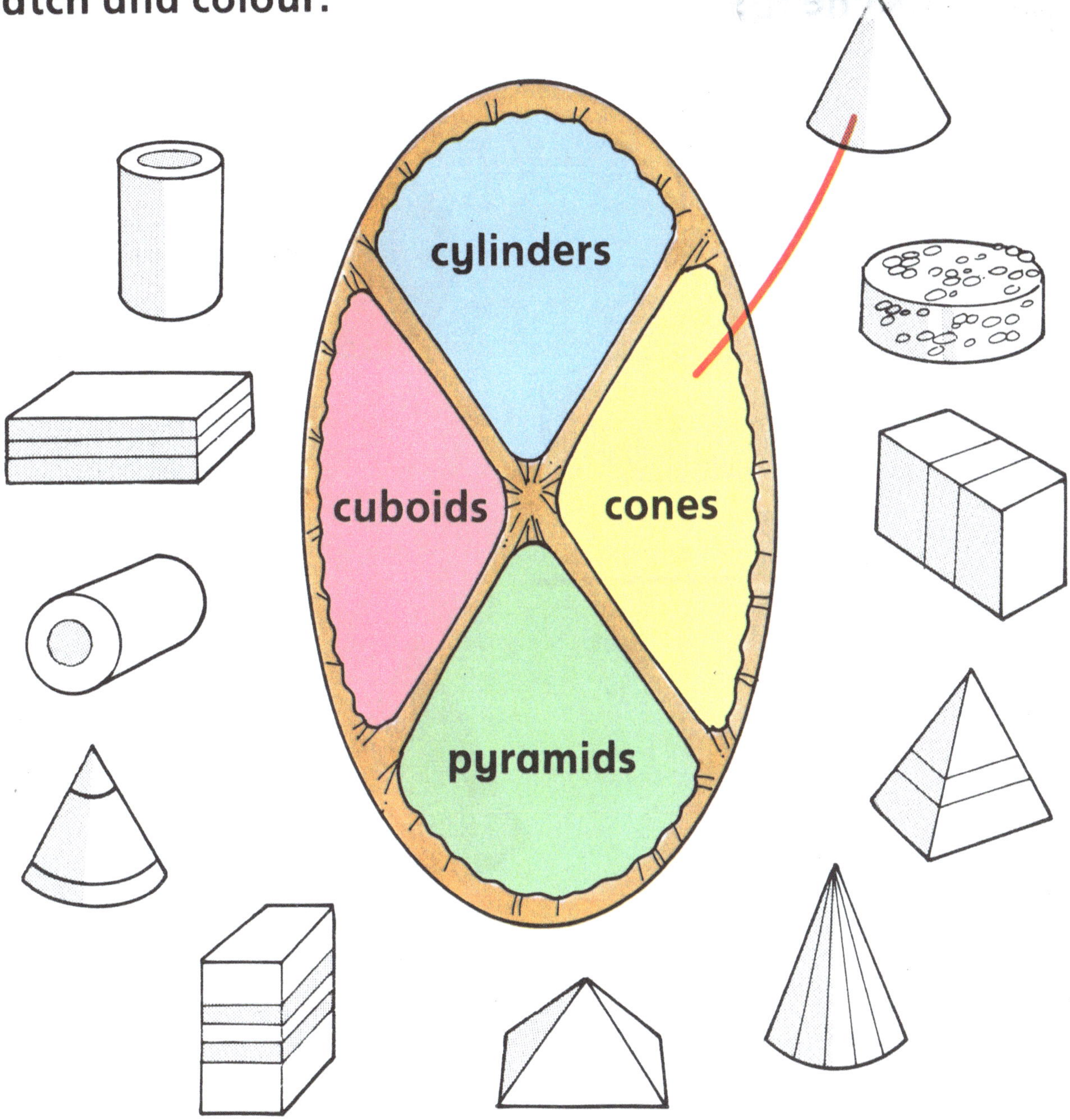

- cylinders
- cuboids
- cones
- pyramids

Put sweets in a box.

All the sweets must have a curved face.

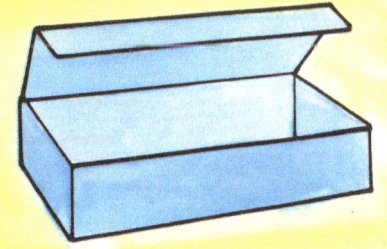

Chocolates

| cube | cone | sphere | cylinder | cuboid | pyramid |

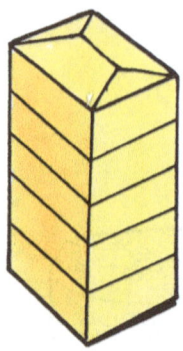

cuboid

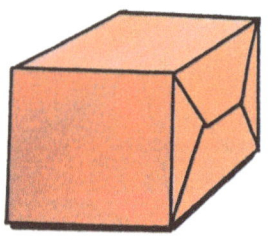

Problem solving — **3D shape pattern**

What comes next?

cone?
pyramid?
sphere?

cuboid?
cylinder?
cone?

pyramid?
sphere?
cube?

Caterpillars

Complete each pattern.

Draw a shape pattern.

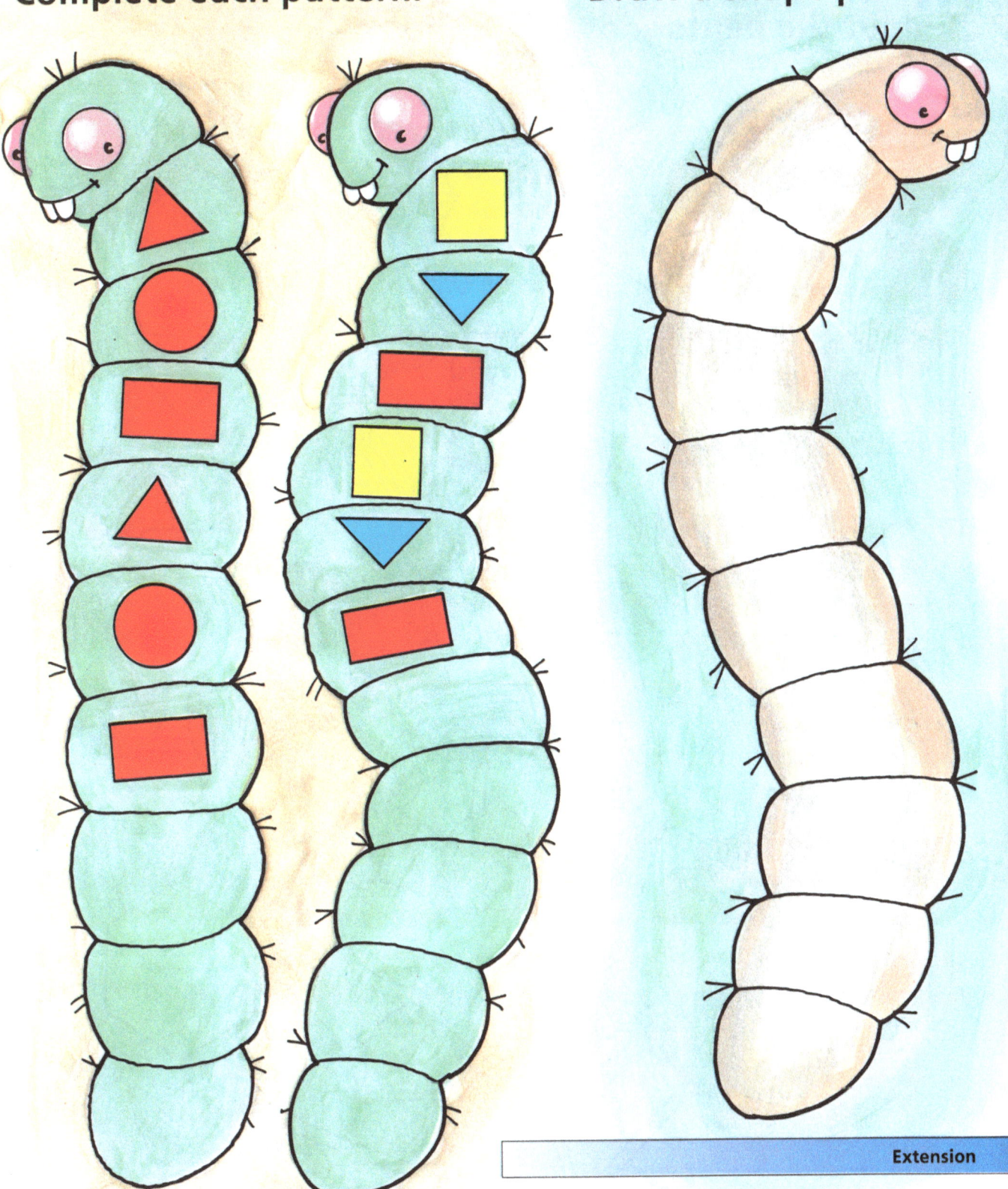

Extension

Make another caterpillar with a pattern.

Flowers

Colour the pentagons and the hexagons.

How many pentagons?

How many hexagons?

Pentagons and hexagons

Colour the pentagons red. Colour the hexagons blue.

How many pentagons?
How many hexagons?

Match

Investigation   2D shape

10 straws

I made these shapes with 10 straws.

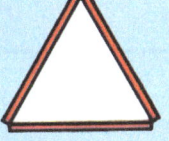      

| triangle | triangle | square |

What shapes can you make with 10 straws? Draw and name them.

11 Right-angles: introduction

Picture

Colour the right-angles.

Right-angles

✗ and count the right-angles.

4

___

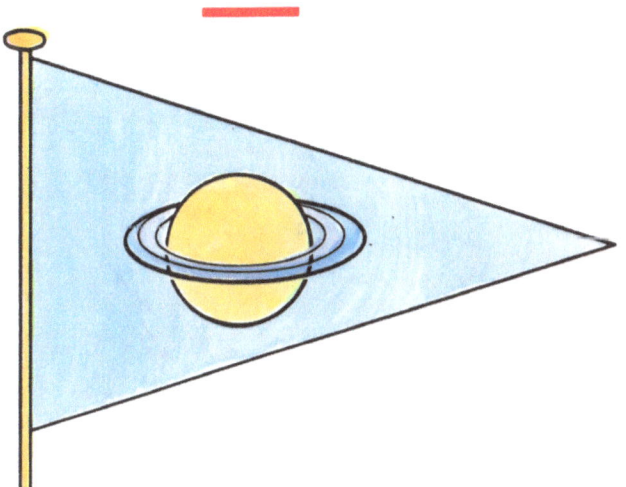

___

___

Right-angle turns

Paths in the forest

Start at

  forward 1
  turn left
  forward 3

Finish at _____

Start at

  forward 10
  back 3
  turn left
  forward 3

Finish at _____

Start at

  forward 3
  turn left
  forward 1
  turn right
  forward 4

Finish at _____

Start at

  forward 4
  turn right
  forward 1
  turn left
  forward 3
  turn left
  forward 2

Finish at _____

Extension

Tell your friend how to go from  cave to  well.

Envelopes

 Jill

 Tom

 Anita

Who flipped it over? _____

Who moved it along? _____

Who turned it round? _____

1	2	3	4	5	6	7	8	9	10	11	12	13	14	15